武満 徹

フルートのための

エア

TORU TAKEMITSU
AIR

for flute

SJ 1096

T0050745

SCHOTT

Air
エ ア
for flute

Toru Takemitsu
武満 徹

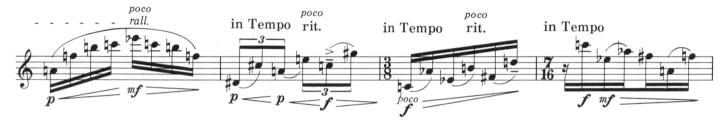
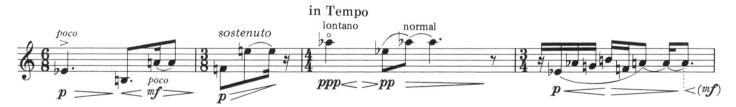

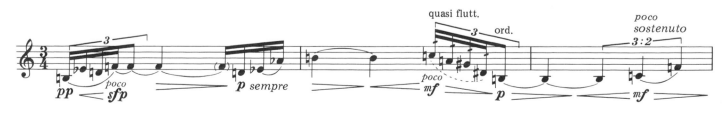

フルートのための《エア》は、1996年1月28日、スイスのバーゼルラント州、オーバーヴィルのカトリック教会で、植村泰一によって初演された。

演奏時間——7分

Air for flute was first performed by Yasukazu Uemura at Katholisch Kirche Oberwil in Baselland, Switzerland on January 28, 1996.

Duration: 7 minutes

ABBREVIATIONS AND SYMBOL:

n.v.　　= Without vibrato
c.v.　　= With vibrato
♮　　　= One quarter-tone lower

CHART OF FINGERING NUMBERS:

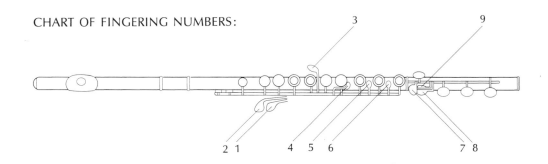

The instrument requires a low B♮.
The trills used in this piece are played at the same pitch. The required fingerings are indicated.

武満 徹《エア》　　　　　　　　　　●

フルートのための

初版発行───────────────── 1996年3月15日

第1版第10刷⑩ ───────────── 2023年4月14日

発行─────────────ショット・ミュージック株式会社

──────────東京都千代田区内神田1-10-1 平富ビル3階

─────────────〒101-0047

─────────────(03)6695-2450

─────────────www.schottjapan.com

─────────────ISBN 978-4-89066-396-5

─────────────ISMN M-65001-012-2

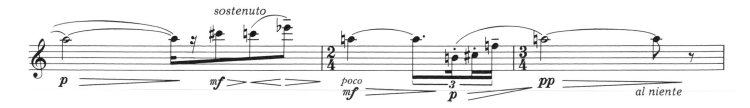

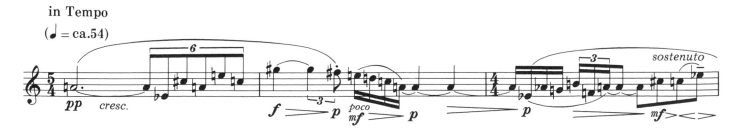

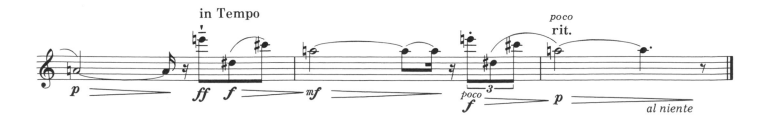

現代の音楽
MUSIC OF OUR TIME

FLUTE

武満 徹　　Toru Takemitsu (1930–1996)

海へ
Toward the Sea
for alto flute and guitar . . . SJ 1007 (performing score) . . . 1500 円

海へ III
Toward the Sea III
for alto flute and harp . . . SJ 1049 (performing score) . . . 2200 円

エア
Air
for flute . . . SJ 1096 . . . 900 円

星たちの息子 ──第一幕への前奏曲「天職」──
Le Fils des Étoiles —Prélude du 1ᵉʳ Acte "La Vocation"—
Transcription for flute and harp of a solo piano work by Eric Satie
SJ 1067 (score & part) . . . 1500 円

巡り ──イサム・ノグチの追憶に──
Itinerant —In Memory of Isamu Noguchi—
for flute . . . SJ 1055 . . . 1000 円

湯浅譲二　　Joji Yuasa (1929–)

タームズ・オヴ・テンポラル・ディーテイリング
──D・ホックニーへのオマージュ──
Terms of Temporal Detailing —A Homage to David Hockney—
for bass flute . . . SJ 1062 . . . 1600 円

ドメイン
Domain
for solo flute . . . SJ 1002 . . . 1000 円

舞働 II
Mai-Bataraki II
for alto flute (or noh flute) . . . SJ 1043 . . . 1000 円

礼楽 ──尹伊桑の追憶に──
Reigaku —In Memoriam Isang Yun—
for alto flute . . . SJ 1137 . . . 900 円

一柳 慧　　Toshi Ichiyanagi (1933–)

時の佇い IV ──武満 徹の追憶に──
Still Time IV —In Memory of Toru Takemitsu—
for flute . . . SJ 1112 . . . 700 円

忘れえぬ記憶の中に
In a Living Memory
for flute solo . . . SJ 1126 . . . 1200 円

高橋悠治　　Yuji Takahashi (1938–)

チッ(ト)
Ji(t)
for flute and piano . . . SJ 1039 (performing score) . . . 1400 円

細川俊夫　　Toshio Hosokawa (1955–)

息の歌
Atem-Lied
for bass flute . . . SJ 1175 . . . 1600 円

垂直の歌
Vertical Song
for flute . . . SJ 1105 . . . 1000 円

線 I
Sen I
for flute . . . SJ 1076 . . . 1700 円

鳥たちへの断章 III
Birds Fragments III
for shô and flutes (bass flute and piccolo) (score & parts) . . . SJ 1146
2300 円

リート
Lied
for flute and piano (score & parts) . . . SJ 1166 . . . 1800 円

ショット・ミュージック株式会社
東京都千代田区内神田1-10-1　平富ビル3階　〒101-0047
電話 (03) 6695-2450　ファクス (03) 6695-2579
sales@schottjapan.com　www.schottjapan.com

SCHOTT MUSIC CO. LTD.
Hiratomi Bldg., 1-10-1 Uchikanda, Chiyoda-ku, Tokyo 101-0047
Telephone: (+81)3-6695-2450　Fax: (+81)3-6695-2579
sales@schottjapan.com　www.schottjapan.com

（価格には消費税が含まれておりません）